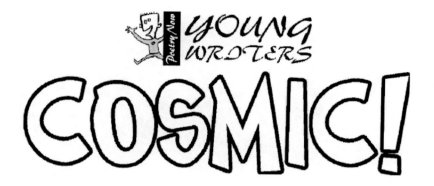

ESSEX VOL II

Edited by Sarah Lester

First published in Great Britain in 1998 by
POETRY NOW YOUNG WRITERS
1-2 Wainman Road, Woodston,
Peterborough, PE2 7BU
Telephone (01733) 230748

HB ISBN 0 75430 185 0
SB ISBN 0 75430 186 9

FOREWORD

With over 63,000 entries for this year's Cosmic competition, it has proved to be our most demanding editing year to date.

We were, however, helped immensely by the fantastic standard of entries we received, and, on behalf of the Young Writers team, thank you.

Cosmic Essex Vol II is a tremendous reflection on the writing abilities of 10 & 11 year old children, and the teachers who have encouraged them must take a great deal of credit.

We hope that you enjoy reading *Cosmic Essex Vol II* and that you are impressed with the variety of poems and style with which they are written, giving an insight into the minds of young children and what they think about the world today.

CONTENTS

St Mary's RC JMI School, Hornchurch

Laura More	60
Rebecca Joy O'Leary	61
Ailish Ginty	62
Lara Freeman	62
Anne Edwards	63
Kelly Rudd	64
Lucy Fleming	64
Stewart Mundy	65
Siobhan Mahoney	65
Danny McEvoy	66
Daniel Alexander	66
Sam Morrison	67
Luke Linehan	68
Natalie Morrison	68
Gemma Hawkins	69
Lucy Flynn	70
Ben Adams	70
Jane Stonell	71
Amy McLeavy	71
Joe Wilson	72
Tyrone Patten-Walsh	72
Damian Jones	73
Christopher Cable	74
Perrie McDowell	74
Craig Midson	75
Daniel Needham	75
Sharlene Power	76
Simon Smith	76
Christine Scott	77
Kelly Gerbaldi	77
Claudio Zeolla	78
Nicola Hawkins	78
Laura Wood	79
Charlotte Carver	80
Claire Chisholm	80
Ainhoa Keskin	81
Gareth Lowe	81

THE POEMS

THE HOUSE ON THE HILL

The garden is still,
Silent is the house,
And all to be heard
Is the drip of the tap
And scurrying of a mouse.

A cat purring while it sleeps,
A dog cries, sniffles and weeps.

As the dawn breaks,
And the cat wakes,
The sun shines brightly,
And you can see,
The frightful old house,
Once silent and still,
Is now a friendly building,
On a green, grass hill.

And when the darkness,
Comes round once again
We shall all know
That it isn't a scary haunted house
But a friendly old building
As scary as a mouse.

Rhiannon Collings (11)
Alderton County Junior School

MY MAGIC BOX

In my magic box I would put
All my favourite books,
'The Chalet School', 'The Famous Five'
So many, take a look!

All my family,
Dad, Mum and Sarah,
People ask why I do this
Why? Because they're the best, they are!

I would put in love
As much as can be,
Everyone needs it
Both you and me!

I would put in joy
Peace and happiness,
Plenty of goodwill
And lots of kindness!

I would put good health
In my magic box,
Bad health and
Wickedness is unorthodox!

In would go my friends
And everything good,
Working and playing
Like we should!

I would put in memories
So we could not part,
Also to remember the
People in my heart!

Rachel Wetherfield (11)
Alderton County Junior School

ASKING QUESTIONS

Mum . . .

Who first used a handwriting pen?
Who made up the first rule?
Why do I have to eat broccoli?
Why on earth do we go to school?

Dad . . .

When was Prit Stick invented?
Where is the land of the ghouls?
Who first scraped chalk down a blackboard?
Who made my friends so cool?

Nan . . .

Were you around with the dinosaurs?
If so, why are they extinct?
And who hunted down the dodo?
Oh, and why do hose-pipes get kinks?

Grandad . . .

When will the sun explode?
Who invented the loo?
Can walls really hear what you're saying?
I don't know the answers, do you?

Laura Cremer (11)
Alderton County Junior School

WHAT ARE YOU?

I'm a car, I'm a car,
A brand-new car,
I'm clean
I'm mean
I'm a driving machine.

I'm a car, I'm a car,
A brand-new car,
I drive around every day
Nothing gets in my way
I'm a driving machine.

I'm a car, I'm a car,
A brand-new car,
I'm fast
I'm vast
I'm a driving machine.

I'm a car, I'm a car,
A brand-new car,
I'm a saloon
I drive till noon
I'm a driving machine.

I'm a car, I'm a car,
A brand-new car,
I don't make a sound
When I'm driving around
I'm a driving machine.

I'm a car, I'm a car,
A brand-new car,
I'm not at all big
But I don't give a fig
I'm a driving machine.

Andrew Hill (10)
Alderton County Junior School

THE TORNADO

The wind was an elephant rushing around
Causing a great calamity.
The tornado spun round like a spinning top
The wind was as cold as icicles
As it sliced through me.
The tornado killed so many people,
I don't know how I lived to tell the tale.

Kirsty Macaulay (10)
Thames View Junior School

THE CAT

Her fur is as white as fresh milk
Her walk is sleek and queenly
Her breath smells like fish bones
The colour of the cat is bronze
with hints of gold like a great treasure
Her eyes are a glowing coal.

Rebecca Martin (10)
Thames View Junior School

THE CAT

Her ears are as pointed as a dagger.
Her eyes are the shape of a crystal.
Her teeth sparkle like stars in the sky.
The eyes are on the lookout for a victim to pounce on.
Her purr is as soft as a flower.

Stacey Knowles (10)
Thames View Junior School

THE CAT

His fur is as soft as leather.
His eyes are like glittery diamonds.
His teeth are like sharp knives.
The tail is big and bushy.
His nose is wet like a puddle.

Alfie Brand-Traverso (10)
Thames View Junior School

A TEACHER'S POINT OF VIEW

Monday morning here they come
The first lesson has begun.

Tuesday morning they're back again
My nightmare has started again.

Wednesdays are just the same
Teachers just want to get out the cane.

Thursday mornings you can't be late
The school bus just can't wait.

Friday, it isn't the same
The children don't act the same.

I wonder why!

Sharanjit Cheema (10)
Thames View Junior School

AUTUMN LEAVES

Leaves twisting, turning fast,
Dancing, spinning, tumbling with a twirl,
Scampering slowly as they fall.
Slow movements along the ground,
As they gently drift among other leaves.
Crunchy, crispy, delicate and dry.
Standing trees shiver in the cold,
As they sway like a skeleton,
Bare and alone.
Red, yellow, orange and brown
Bright and dull,
As the sun shines on.
The leaves are now picked up by the wind,
And they shine their colours,
With a twist,
  A turn,
   A swirl,
    A whirl
     A dance
      And a spin until they're exhausted.
      They fly to a corner to
         gently rest.

Kelly Jarvis (11)
Thames View Junior School

EASTER EGG

Have you eaten an Easter egg?
The one that's full with chocolate,
The one that turns you round and round,
And whizzes you to the ground.

Kelly Tyler (11)
Thames View Junior School

AUTUMN IS HERE!

Autumn is here at last.
The leaves are different colours.
Yellow, orange, brown, red and golden.
Animals are starting to hibernate.
They are going in for their winter's rest.
The trees are now naked and bare.
All the leaves are making a carpet on the ground.
Dead!
Then a gust of wind blows,
They come alive,
They dance, pirouette their way through the sky.
The wind drops.
The leaves are now exhausted.
The wind picks up speed
Leaves are swirling, spiralling
and then they tumble to the
ground with a gentle thud.
		Autumn has left.

Nicola Lillywhite (11)
Thames View Junior School

THE CAT

His eyes are like honey
His fur is silver
His teeth are shining like stars
The nose of a pig
His ears, soft like marshmallows.

Louise Fox (10)
Thames View Junior School

ALL FRIENDS

I love my friends like family.
Friendship is forever
For you and me
Please don't row
Please don't fight
I dream about you every night.
It's raining lots of Jelly Tots
Like friendship up above
I can see you flying like a
                    turtle dove.

Toni Furby (10)
Thames View Junior School

THE LEAVES OF AUTUMN

Dancing, swaying, leaves everywhere.
Tumbling down off the skeleton trees.
Fragile, dry, crunchy,
Rustling and flapping everywhere.
Drifting, whirling, floating
Orange, brown, red
Dancing swiftly along the pavement.

Shahnaz Khalique (11)
Thames View Junior School

AUTUMN

Autumn is coming
Leaves starting to change colour,
Sunset red, golden yellow and rusty brown
They tumble, spin and dance through the air.
Animals go to sleep,
The long winter ahead,
Trees give up their leaves
Tree like a brown skeleton, standing there,
Now autumn has gone and winter is here.

Laura Sydney-Smith (10)
Thames View Junior School

CRISPY, CRUNCHY LEAVES

Tumbling, swinging, crispy, dry leaves
Branches like a skeleton waving in the wind.
Bare and shivering.
Leaves dancing, tumbling, like snowflakes,
Swinging, twisting, crispy, crunchy,
Dry, red, brown, yellow leaves
Scampering along the street.
Whistling through the air,
Leaves in corners like a cat sleeping
          Wind blowing, roaring like a bear.

Timothy Hunt (11)
Thames View Junior School

COLOURS OF AUTUMN

Autumn is here.
The leaves are crispy, crunchy and dry,
Orange, red, yellow, golden, brown.
Tumbling, fluttering like a butterfly,
Leaving the trees bare.
Waving like a skeleton at night.
Then the leaves hang together,
The wind blows at them.
All the leaves start to whirl and tumble
As the wind howls.
Then they fall to the floor and all is quiet.

Lisa Beason (10)
Thames View Junior School

AUTUMN LEAVES

Tumbling, dancing in the sky,
Swiftly falling, swirling around.
Gently floating.
Reds, yellows, browns
Bright and dull.
The fragile leaves dry and crisp,
Leaving the trees bare and empty.

Melanie Puttnam (10)
Thames View Junior School

SPACE POEMS

J   ust in the sky,
U   p up high,
P   lanet you must see,
I   s it good enough for me?
T   he stars shining so bright,
E   arth is so light,
R   ockets shooting by.

P   lanets up high,
L   urking about the sky,
A   liens on the ground,
N   ever to be found,
E   arth is far away,
T   hinking of home, I pray,
S   tars twinkling on by.

S   tars shining all around,
T   rying to light up the ground,
A   liens going back to space,
R   ockets flying around the place,
S   eeing what can be found.

Gemma Doak (11)
Thames View Junior School

THE CAT

Her stripy fur is like a spiky hedgehog.
Her eyes glitter in the moonlight.
Her tail is like a cobra,
The cat hunts for mice,
Her teeth are as sharp as a saw.

Sheltan Lewis (10)
Thames View Junior School

AUTUMN

Look at those leaves,
Falling down,
Twisting, turning,
Crackling,
Conkers falling everywhere,
Wind blowing in my face strong
as heavy weights,
That's why I've got naked trees
in my back garden,
Sweeping all the leaves out of my back
garden when autumn goes.

Gemma Julia Chance (11)
Thames View Junior School

FIREWORK NIGHT

Bang, crackle, noise in the air,
Smoke and coloured light everywhere,
Standing with excitement in the cold,
People of all ages, young and old,
Firework night should be fun,
Take care, be safe and you'll live,
              to see another one.

Aaron Smith (11)
Thames View Junior School

THE DAY OF DISASTER

Trouble was not far away
On that bad disastrous day.

In the morning
At half-past eight,
I woke up yawning
I'd slept too late.
The bread in the toaster
I'm trying to cope,
Then suddenly the room
Fills up with smoke.

Trouble was not far away
On that bad disastrous day.

I'm running to school
The rain pouring down.
I'm soaked when I'm there
My face stuck in a frown.
I was ten minutes late
I tried my best,
It got worse when I failed
My spelling test.

Trouble was not far away
On that bad disastrous day.

Daniel Wheeler (11)
Thames View Junior School

IN THE LOFT

In the loft it is dark and cold.
It smells like rotten old mould.
I hear groaning and moaning,
Then shots and bangs.

In the loft it's damp and stinky,
I hear yells and screams.
Nobody ever goes up there,
Only if it's a dare.

Nikita Laurence (10)
Thames View Junior School

FLYING

Flying leaves flying
like a
plane gliding
through the
sky
Big white bubbles
surrounding it
Flying, flying
and the
wind
stops
and the
leaves float
down
s
l
o
w
l
y

David Routley (11)
Thames View Junior School

AUTUMN

Golden, brown, red leaves.
Tumbling, twisting, dancing to the wet ground.
Naked trees shiver in the cold and wind,
Damp crisp leaves cover the hard floor.

Small animals, squirrels, badgers,
Collecting nuts and berries and food.
Getting ready for a freezing winter,
Hibernating in a deep sleep.

Jake Wheeler (11)
Thames View Junior School

AUTUMN LEAVES

Autumn is here,
Leaves fall off trees.
Oranges, yellows, browns, some golden and rusty.
Leaves fall off branches,
Then drift gently down to the earth,
Floating around trees,
Around and around,
Then drop like a tear.
Now the trees are bare and autumn has gone,
Winter is here.

Amardeep Bains (10)
Thames View Junior School

AUTUMN IS HERE

Autumn leaves swaying on the branches
Golden like gold itself
Red, even redder than a ruby.
Brown as brown as mud
Whirling, twisting through the air
like a gymnast on the bars
Some as fast as a helter-skelter
Some as soft and gentle as a graceful swan.
The trees are bare and naked as a skeleton
Animals start collecting food for the winter
All the squirrels, bears, rabbits and many more.
Harvest is here,
All the farmers collect their grain to earn
their money in the market place.

Kyle Olajorin (11)
Thames View Junior School

COLOURS OF AUTUMN

Leaves red, leaves brown.
Leaves falling all over the ground.
Leaves fragile, leaves dry,
Leaves flying through the sky.

Daniel Domingo (10)
Thames View Junior School

THE SPINNING LEAVES

Autumn is here at last!
All of the leaves are different colours,
Gold, rusty, red and yellow
Animals are starting to hibernate
Leaves are falling down
The trees are bare they look just like a skeleton
The leaves dance and the trees shiver
The tree is now naked
As the leaves fall, they look like sparrows
All the leaves make a carpet on the floor.

Robert Rainey (10)
Thames View Junior School

COLOURS OF AUTUMN

Orange, red, yellow and golden leaves.
Twisting like a helter-skelter falling to the ground.
They drift gently and sway high, low, side to side.
As I walk upon the leaves they go *crunch, crunch, crunch!*
The leaves are like the colour of an old tin can
Which has been left out in the rain.

Claire Louise Veazey (10)
Thames View Junior School

DANCING LEAVES

Flying through the air
Like blind bats
Falling from the trees,
Like the water from a waterfall.
Rustling on the ground,
Like an empty crisp packet.
These leaves which are as
rusty as an old bike,
get whisked by the wind,
                    Far, far, away!

Pierre Nii Amarte Godson-Amamoo (10)
Thames View Junior School

AUTUMN IS COMING

The colours of autumn leaves are
brown, orange and red.
The trees are black.
Leaves are flying in the air, dancing and twisting.
The dry leaves fall like a helter-skelter
tumbling and spinning.
The flapping, flittering leaves fall rustling,
Crunchy, crisp leaves on the ground.
I like to walk on the crunchy, crispy leaves.

Susan Marney (10)
Thames View Junior School

DELICATE LEAVES

Delicate, fragile, dead brown leaves,
Trees naked shivering in the cold wind.
Dancing round with the whirling wind,
The leaves get exhausted and rest.
As they rest they scrunch when someone steps on them.
Conkers fall to the ground and break.
Now here comes a breeze.
Leaves start pirouetting, swirling, whirling.
The breeze gets stronger.
Leaves start flying through the streets.
The breeze slows down.
Now autumn begins to fade.

Judy Edwards (11)
Thames View Junior School

AUTUMN LEAVES

Autumn is coming.
Leaves rustling on the tree waiting to come off.
Wind comes whirling in and knocks off the leaves.
Leaves dancing, swaying, drifting around and around.
Leaves swaying in the wind.
Gently they land on earth and go into a corner.
They huddle together.
Conkers fall and crack out of their shell.
The trees are like a skeleton, *bare.*

Sam Ross (11)
Thames View Junior School

AUTUMN LEAVES

Autumn is coming,
Orange, brown, red leaves falling.
Crunchy delicate leaves falling off the trees.
The animals are hibernating,
The harvest is here,
Trees are all naked.
The leaves swirl, turn, tumble and dance.
Spinning in circles, falling to the ground
Where they're left to scamper.
The tree, bare and naked, stands in the cold.

Charlie-Anne Day (10)
Thames View Junior School

AUTUMN LEAVES

Golden, yellow, orange, red.
The leaves go to bed.
In the morning they dance and twist.
They sway and spin so gently.
Rustling, shivering as they fall.
Twisting slowly as they fall.
Flapping at night and spinning down.
Hatching conkers fall from the tree.
The birds fly south, and the animals go home.

Winter is here!

Colin Peterson (11)
Thames View Junior School

THE LEAVES FALL DOWN

Tumbling, twisting, spinning, dancing, swirling,
like a helter-skelter,
Spinning down very fast,
Pirouetting from corner to corner.
Jumping about like a gymnast,
Flying about like a beautiful butterfly
fluttering in the air.
As the leaves say goodbye to the tree,
they look back and see the bare, naked
shivering tree, that looks like he has just
had his coat torn off him.
He has to stand there on the very
windy and cold night.
Then the leaves go to a corner
                              and rest.

Jay Pope (11)
Thames View Junior School

AUTUMN IS HERE

Leaves turn slowly and begin to fall
They twist slowly in the air.
They start to float.
They begin to drift slowly.
When they hit the ground
The leaves start to turn brown.
The tree becomes naked
The tree freezes.

Lloyd Holliday (10)
Thames View Junior School

AUTUMN IS HERE

Autumn is here.
Leaves all brown and crispy, fly
through the sky like a sweet
little butterfly.
Crunchy, crispy, rustling leaves twist,
through the trees with the gentle breeze.

Nikki Pope (11)
Thames View Junior School

AUTUMN

Autumn leaves fall to the floor.
Yellow, red, green and plenty more.
Children run and dive in leaves.
Dogs go barking at the trees.
Squirrels look for nuts so they can feed.
Children dress up all warm so they don't
feel the autumn cold.
Woolly hats, gloves and all
are the things you need for autumn fall.
Trees are bare, no leaves left at all.
Trees rest until spring.
Chilly nights, frost and all that, the beginning
of autumn fall.

Joe Martin (11)
The Greensward School

SPRING

Daffodils are growing,
Primroses appearing,
Hedgehogs coming out of hibernation,
Green buds on the trees,
It's Spring.

Frisky lambs jumping about,
Baby chicks being born,
Children running about in joy,
The sun shining, warming the world,
It's Spring.

It's Spring, it's Spring,
No more wind, rain, snow,
Just beach, sun, and fun,
It's Spring.

Danielle Russo (11)
The Greensward School

PARENTS

They shout,
They yell,
Make your life a living hell,
They scream,
All the time,
You'd think it was a crime
To leave mouldy socks lying around.

Tidy your room,
Do the washing up,
Don't you dare leave that cup,
In your room.

Look at your hair,
How on earth can you bear,
That ghastly green mop,
On your head?

That's not a top,
It's a belt,
No, you can't wear it out tonight,
You'll give the neighbours a fright.

Samantha Daly (11)
The Greensward School

MY BEST FRIEND

E mma is so good to me,
M aking me laugh all the time.
M essing around with her friends,
A bsolutely the best friend in the world.

S hy and quiet, that is what she is,
T akes me to school, that is very kind.
O ccasionally she is grumpy,
N ice and caring.
E veryone likes her.

Keeley Gatward (11)
The Greensward School

FOX HUNTING

Hungry and sad in his den,
He hears a stampede above his head.
What a terrible fear he has for men.

He hears a horn sound bright and clear,
And then the bark of growling dogs.
They seemed to be getting close and near.

Then all is silent, not a sound,
Should he chance it and make the run,
Or should he stay safe underground?

He climbs cautiously out and runs,
Then the sound of galloping hooves.
The shots of guns.

Then the hunters pass, all is still,
The fox lies stiff and dead.
Just think of how he ran with all his will.

How cruel we all are just killing for sport,
They just left the poor thing ice-cold dead.
Why don't we give a care and thought?

Heidi Young (11)
The Greensward School

BREAKFAST WITH THE STARS

The magical land of Disney,
A dream at first,
But then it came,
Breakfast with the stars.

> We sit down at our table,
> Look around, and around again,
> 'Mum, I can't see them, where are they?'
> Breakfast with the stars.

Then, I suddenly see one of them!
They come over and sit down next to me,
They shake my hand, take a picture,
Breakfast with the stars.

> They autograph my book,
> And give me a cuddle,
> Some put in messages,
> Breakfast with the stars.

I couldn't see the main star,
Then he came running in,
He came over and sat down next to me,
Breakfast with the stars,

> He put in a message,
> And that message said,
> 'From your pal, Mickey Mouse!'
> Breakfast with the Disney stars.

James Caldon (11)
The Greensward School

TITANIC

Titanic the unsinkable ship,
was everybody's dream,
this was what people were waiting for,
everyone was keen.

The captain shouted 'All aboard,'
everyone got on,
the ship started to sail away,
some sang a cheerful song.

'Whether we are upper class,
whether we are lower class,
we could always have a glass
of Titanic's finest wine.'

Until one day,
disaster struck,
they were hit by an iceberg
'Twas very bad luck.

The ship was starting to sink,
as a result of a hole in the side,
everyone jumping off,
these people were going to die.

Titanic plunged,
down to the seabed,
over 1500 people died,
or so it was said.

The dream ship,
now lies at the bottom of the sea,
all those memories,
was this really meant to be?

Nicola O'Keeffe & Danielle Underwood (12)
The Greensward School

MY GRANDAD

My grandad was the best
Better than any of the rest
He was really, really kind
He was also good at bowls you'll find
He loved everybody the same
Whether they were exciting or plain
I wish he would come back again
Even though he is now out of pain.

Sophie Coubrough (11)
The Greensward School

TOPSY-TURVY WORLD

Uranus the planet that's been pushed on its side,
Its blue clouds of methane are nice,
Miranda is a small moon out of five,
Then comes Umbriel and Ariel,
Oberon and Tatania are more,
But most of all I would like to know,
How did it become topsy-turvy?

Did someone start a football match?
Or start a tennis game?
Maybe somebody hit it with their rocket ship?
Or possibly it could have been aliens.

I would freeze to death on your planet,
That's why I don't visit you,
I want to stay on my planet,
You want to stay on your planet,
I don't want to join your planet
And you don't want to join mine.

Georgina Chase (10)
Grove County Junior School

LET'S PROBE THE UNIVERSE

Comets zooming across the sky
visible to the naked eye
They seem dazzling to you and I
Let's probe the Universe.

Astronauts are having a race
to see who lives longest in outer space
they've even built a permanent base
Let's probe the Universe.

Stars and planets by the score
Each time we look there's more and more
as through the galaxy we soar
Let's probe the Universe.

Flying saucers roam the stars
They land on Earth, they land on Mars
They steal all the 'Milky Bars'
Let's probe the Universe!

Those aliens like all things sweet
It makes them glow from head to feet
The more they find, the more they eat
Let's probe the Universe!

The final frontier looms ahead
as I lie sleeping in my bed
we'll keep on probing until we're dead
Let's probe the Universe!

James Rooke (10)
Grove County Junior School

THE WIND AND THE WORLD

The wind is a ship sailing right out to sea,
The wind is a lover coming right back to me.
The wind is a song being played by a band,
The wind is a tidal wave being blown through the land,
The wind is a barrier protecting the world,
The wind is a toy for boys and girls,
The wind is all these things and more,
Blowing across the world's green floor.

John Hawker (11)
Grove County Junior School

BLUE

As blue as the ink I write with,
As blue as the sea
the sky
the rain.
As blue as pencil pots
the language box.
As blue as the handwriting books
folders, trays, my bedroom.
As blue as ice-cream tubs
towels, camp bags, cup, plate and bowl.
I like blue.

Martin Williamson (10)
Hacton JM&I School

ICE HOCKEY MANIA

Shoot the puck,
At the net,
What's the score?
No goal yet.
Padded arms,
Hard-hat heads
Gum shield in,
Protected legs.
Ice-skates on,
Stick in hand,
Penalty shot.
Still I stand.
Team-mates shout
And coaches scream
Soon to be over,
Who's the winning team?
The whistle's blown,
I start to skate,
Before I know it I'm everybody's mate.
The puck went in,
My team has won,
Now the new score is one to none.
We are the winners,
We are the best
We've had victory
We're better than the rest.

Terri Shepherd (11)
Hacton JM&I School

MY FIRST DAY AT SCHOOL

It was my first day at school,
I never knew anyone,
I stood next to my mummy,
Until the bell had rung,
I met my new teacher,
Her name was Mrs Dyal,
She was tall with long golden hair,
She always had a smile.
I met my new classmates,
There were lots of girls and boys,
They hung up their coats,
Then trotted inside.
I was scared and frightened,
But I walked in calmly,
I clung on to my mother's arm,
While children stared at me,
The time went whizzing by,
I was having so much fun,
We played games in the playground,
After our work was done,
I made so many friends
Which was really good,
I tried to fit in as best I could,
I went to sleep that night,
And thought of what I'd done.
I couldn't wait until tomorrow,
For another day of fun!

Katie O'Sullivan
Hacton JM&I School

I CAN SEE THE WORLD

I am an eagle,
I am the greatest bird of all,
I fly very high,
The people look so small,
As I swoop down to the trees,
A poacher waits for me,
With a rifle in his hand,
How deadly can he be?
The poacher raises his gun,
He aims it at my side,
He missed me by an inch,
Or else I could have died,
I fly back to my eyrie,
Now I'm safe and sound,
In amongst the cliffs,
High above the ground.

Katie O'Sullivan (11)
Hacton JM&I School

NETBALL POEM

Netball is fun,
Netball is great,
Netball is when I started at eight,
Netball is where you pass the ball,
Netball is where I play at school,
Netball is cool,
Netball is enjoying,
Netball is never ever boring,
Netball is good, will you join with me?

Netball, netball, is all I do,
Netball, netball, is great for you,
Netball is what I like so much,
I catch the ball
I throw the ball and try to score as well,
Netball is where I play with my mates.

Stacey Palmer (10)
Hacton JM&I School

BLACK

As black as darkness
Clouds going across
the full moon
Black fizzy Coke popping out
like a black fountain
spreading everywhere.
As black as a spider
tickling your arm
'Ouch!'
As black as a witch
zooming on her magic
broom laughing
Ha, ha, ha!
As black as black coffee
steaming up like smoke.
Black chocolate melting on
my hand like mud!
Black numbers on the
clock
telling it's time to come
home.

Lauren Smith (11)
Hacton JM&I School

DAY-DREAMING

Mrs Butcher thinks I'm
watching her signing
but I'm not
I'm
thinking of meeting the
people who play in
Casualty
And I dream of
working for
The St John's Division
and the National Red Cross
I'm working for 999
with Michael Burke
I'm meeting Michael Knight
in Knight-Rider 2000
and visiting St Vincent
to see my nan and grandad
It's hot and boiling
but at night
it gets really cold
I'm going to London
to see my Grandma
and Reuben and Ivan
my cousins
I wake up
I find myself alone
everyone has gone to

Playtime . . .

Tamsin Francis (11)
Hacton JM&I School

DAY-DREAMS

I'm in Paris
Disneyland is the best
Hi Mickey!
Nobody knows I'm here
I've seen the Spice Girls.
Shake my head
Do it right
Exciting things happened that night
I go to the pictures
With my friends
When I wake up
Mum is back.

Zara-Jayne Arnold (10)
Hacton JM&I School

AS BLACK AS

As black as nightfall when I go to bed.
I hear nothing but the silence but in my dreams I see . . .
As black as a witch's hat, who cackles in the night.
As black as a cat that purrs by the fireside.
As black as a chimney sweep who kisses the bride.
As black as the pupil in your eye which helps you see the world.
As black as a pirate's patch on his eye which makes him look so evil.
As black as a panther in the jungle who stalks his prey by night and day.
As black as a blackbird who swoops down to catch his dinner.
As black as a cab that drives around all day.
As black as tarmac on the road which guides my way.
As black as night until the day.

Michelle Greenoff (10)
Hacton JM&I School

BIRTHDAY

My birthday is coming and I know what I'd like.
I don't want a football or a whistle or a bike.
I don't ask for much Mum, and I won't nag!

No. I don't mean a toy Mum.
I mean one that's real.
An engine! A motor! A fast set of wheels.
I'd buy the petrol if you'd get me a car.
I'd drive very slowly and I wouldn't go far.

Now don't start shouting, Mum.
Don't make a fuss.
I don't want a lorry or a tractor or bus.
Just a little motor car.
It needn't be new, I'm sure that you'll
agree with me when you've thought it through.

What are you saying, Mum?
You've got to be how old?
And what's a driving licence, Mum?
Well, I was never told.
It seemed a good idea Mum, but I will use my brain
Now I've had a little think Mum,
                    what about a plane?

James Smith (10)
Hacton JM&I School

THE NIGHT BEFORE CHRISTMAS

Snow is falling
Frost is freezing
You hear Father Christmas
Coming down your chimney
Reindeers are working quickly
For you on Christmas Eve.

Snow is falling
Frost is freezing
Presents are wrapped
Under the tree
I cannot wait till
Morning to see what
Father Christmas brought
                    for me.

Charlie Young (10)
Hacton JM&I School

OPPOSITES

As light as a white feather
Floating on the cool air.
As heavy as an over-grown elephant
Stomping on the heavy ground.
As tidy as the beautiful room can be,
When the beauty's not tired.
As messy and sloppy can the thing be,
When the untidy wrecks everything.
As hot as the bright sun
Burning you red and brown,
As cold as a frozen ice-cube
From the frozen freezing fridge.
As the light clouds go by
It's really really good.
As the night dreams come
It goes by.
As strong as a muscle man
The beauty uses the muscles.
As weak as a newborn lamb
Learning how to walk.

Nicola April Worsfold (10)
Hacton JM&I School

OPPOSITES

As light as a pearl
Floating down.
As heavy as a hippopotamus
Jumping up and down.
As hot as an oven
Burning all around.
As cold as an ice-cube
Freezing you all the time.
As light as the yellow
Sun shining very bright.
As dark as at black night
And you can't see.
As strong as a big muscle man
As weak as a little brown mouse.

Elizabeth Warren (10)
Hacton JM&I School

DAY-DREAMING

My mum thinks I'm doing my homework
But I'm not . . .
I'm diving in the deep blue sea with dolphins
Or scuba-diving with sharks

Mrs Snow thinks I'm listening
But I'm not . . .
I'm a professional footballer
Or kicking the ball to Ronaldo

My dad thinks I'm watching TV
But I'm not . . .
I'm singing with the Backstreet Boys,
Or getting All Saints' autographs

My brother thinks I'm listening to him
But I'm not . . .
I'm skiing in Lake Tahoe
Or it's my birthday every day.

Mark Harrison & Paul Finch (10)
Hacton JM&I School

DAY-DREAMING

Mrs Snow thinks I'm listening
But I'm not . . .
I'm kicking a ball at Wembley
in an FA Cup Final.
My mum thinks I'm watching television
But I'm not . . .
I'm wearing a West Ham shirt
in the West Ham Merchandise
Booklet for season 1998-1999.
My mum thinks I'm in bed
But I'm not . . .
I've just passed the ball to
Alan Shearer and he's scored
the winning goal for England
in the World Cup.

Adam Tott (10)
Hacton JM&I School

THE DRAGON

I'm a very big dragon
In a very big cave
In the very big cave
There's a very big chest
Of treasure.
I guard it day and night
No one ever goes there
Because they'll get a fright
I am the dragon
And I'm fierce
So no one comes near.

Grant A Green (10)
Hacton JM&I School

DAY-DREAM

Mrs Snow thinks I'm listening
But I'm not!
I'm a famous superstar in the hot beautiful
Caribbean,
Or strolling on the hot sandy beach
And swimming in the deep blue beautiful sea.
My brothers think I'm listening
But I'm not!
I'm drifting along on the white fluffy clouds
Or meeting up with the hot fiery sun.

Lauren Mills (10)
Hacton JM&I School

NATURE

As light as a butterfly
As sharp as a shark
As fat as a hippo
As stripy as a zebra
As fierce as a lion
As green as grass
As furry as a dog
As blue as the sky
As hot as the sun
As spotty as a Dalmation
As bright as a star
As small as a mouse
As big as an elephant
As funny as a clown
As shiny as a coin
As exciting as a game
As brown as wood
As white as paper
As noisy as music
As cuddly as a toy
As beautiful as a rose
As warm as a jumper
As cold as the freezer
As crazy as football
As clever as a teacher
As scary as Goosebumps.

Ashok Ravichandran (10)
Hacton JM&I School

MY GRANDAD

My grandad is far away
But he still loves me
I see him some Saturdays
He wears glasses to see.

My grandad is getting closer
He has a white shiny car
He helped me draw a poster
And now he's not far.

My grandad is around the bend
I'm getting everything ready
I've got some things that he can mend
I can't wait to show him my teddy.

My grandad is here
I'm so glad
Because there's no fear
When he's here I'm never sad.

My grandad has gone
Everything is quiet
Until the next time he comes.

Katy Murphy (11)
Hacton JM&I School

OPPOSITES

As wet as a chattering dolphin
splashing around the sea.
As dry as a rock
on top of a cliff top.
As light as a feather
floating happily in the breezy air.
As heavy as an overgrown elephant
waiting greedily for its food.
As hot as the hot golden sun
burning you brown and bright red.
As cold as the cold snow
covering the land very quickly.
As happy as a child
when he's playing.
As sad as a lonely person
with no friends to talk to.
As weak as a baby lamb
squealing for its mum.
As strong as the world's strongest man
picking two cars up at once.

Lee Smith (11)
Hacton JM&I School

THE MOCKING BIRD AND THE TREE

It stands in the park with its tall and dark,
Branches that sway in the wind
And have you heard, the sweet mocking bird
That sings even when it's not spring?
That is the bird that strengthens the tree
With its sweet-sounding song,
And hearing this song this wonderful song
Helps the old tree along.

Some people laugh at this queer thing
And just walk away
But this is no bother to the mocking bird
He still comes every day.

Sometimes I drop by after school
To hear this lovely song
Now I've got so used to it
I even hum along
So if you ever hear and see
The mocking bird and the tree
I hope you will sit down and maybe even stay a while.

Nisha Oza (10)
Nightingale Primary School

FEELINGS

Feeling happy feeling sad
Feeling rather glad

Feeling under the weather today
Feeling like a rainy day

Feeling happy feeling sad
Feeling rather glad

Feeling just like the sun today
Feeling very gay

Feeling happy feeling sad
Feeling rather glad

Feeling like a broken heart
Feelings broken apart

Feeling happy feeling sad
Feeling rather glad

Feeling like a shining light
Feeling very bright

Feeling happy feeling sad
Feeling rather glad

Samantha James (11)
Nightingale Primary School

LET'S SAY SOMETHING ABOUT 'U'

Without the letter *'U'*
We can't have a word for Universe.
Without the letter *'U'*,
Nobody will go to University,
So I say thank you *(u)*
U, is a letter we can all use
So use the letter *'U'*.

Junior Laoye (10)
Nightingale Primary School

ACROSTIC POEM

L ovely little sister
I   in the country park
T oday she wants to go to the swings
T hough she went on them yesterday
L aughing all the time
E ven when it's raining.

S plashing on her little head
I   n the country park
S o we're going home
T oday she's going to
E at radishes and
R aspberries.

Charlotte McCall (10)
St Alban's School, Hornchurch

ACROSTIC POEM

I ce-skating is my favourite sport,
C ome and see me skate around,
E very Saturday I meet my friend.

S kating around on the ice,
K ids play on,
A nd adults too.
T aking time to practise,
I n the morning,
N ow I am in Grade Six,
G oing up very soon.

Charlotte Hutchison (10)
St Alban's School, Hornchurch

ACROSTIC POEM

N etball's fun for
E veryone
T alent's needed in football
B alance is really bad
A nd
L earning to play and to
L and and put the ball in the net.

Victoria Tomlinson (10)
St Alban's School, Hornchurch

THE STORY OF MY HUNT FOR FOOD
BY BIG-BIG-HEAD

I was very hungry and very weak,
Food was little, 'cause to find it Dad must seek,
I needed just a little bit more to eat,
Just one extra tiny treat.

So I crept out of bed one dark night,
It is hard not to make noise without a light.
But I am very careful and I know my room well,
So my brothers wouldn't wake up and they wouldn't tell.

I crept to the kitchen,
I took a yam,
But I tripped on my way back,
There was a very big *bang!*

My father has caught me,
I've been punished for it too,
I can't play with all my friends,
What am I to do?

Marie O'Riordan (10)
St Alban's School, Hornchurch

ACROSTIC POEM

D olphins are sweet
O r cute
L ike newborn puppies.
P ut dolphins in my
H eart and they will stay in there forever.
I n go the dolphins, out go the sharks.
N othing will stop a dolphin going in my heart.

Siobhan Grady (10)
St Alban's School, Hornchurch

MY FRIEND

I've got a funny friend
Who drives me round the bend
She's a freckled person
With grey-blue eyes
And has liveliness that never dies.

She's got a great sense of humour
But sometimes she's serious
Even when she's serious
She knows when to laugh.

She's adventurous
She's naughty
But only with her friend
The other times she drives
Her friends round the bend.

Claire Pyne (11)
St Francis RC School, Maldon

SCHOOL DINNERS

School dinners are the most revolting food.
We have them fried, mashed, grilled or stewed.
Some days we have macaroni cheese
But mostly we have stuff that's been freezed.
We sometimes have cabbage that's turned horrible and blue
But if we are lucky we have warmed-up stew.
Occasionally we get served things that are out of date,
So normally I give my helpings to my best mate.
If we are bad we get no dessert,
But if we are good we get juicy, succulent pud!

Ella Corrigan (11)
St Francis RC School, Maldon

THE SPROUT

Doctor said
>> there's no
>>>> way out,
You've got
>> a sprout
>>>> without a doubt.
It will take a day or three,
To turn that sprout into a tree.
Why on earth you ate that seed
Is very strange,
>> it is,
>>>> indeed,
You'll have to
>> take pills every day,
Or that sprout won't go away.

But then the growing all took place,
>> Out came a tree right through her
>>>> *face!*

Danielle Attreed (11)
St Francis RC School, Maldon

BULLYING

Every night in bed I laid
Every day I was afraid
Praying to God as I knelt
Only God knew how I felt.

Everyone told me to overcome my fear
What usually helped was a pint of beer
Nobody knows how much it does hurt
For a 6ft-4 bloke to throw you in some dirt.

My mum and dad do not know
They just say 'Go with the flow.'
They don't take it seriously enough
But this bully is very tough.

But now I know I can compromise
I stood up to him and looked him right in the eyes.

John Wilesmith (11)
St Francis RC School, Maldon

THE BULLY

As I approach the corner,
To the nightmare road,
My legs turn to jelly,
I come out in a cold sweat.
Never knowing where he is going to be,
Behind the postbox?
Down a pathway?
Wherever he is,
It's the same thing,
Give your lunch money,
Now!
Biff! Thud! Bash!
And I go without my lunch.
My brothers ignore me,
My friends don't care.
When will this end?
In a week?
Tomorrow?
In a month?
Or never?

James Robinson (11)
St Francis RC School, Maldon

SUNRISE

I see the sun climbing over the hills
It looks beautiful
The colours are of so many shades
Which blend into each other
Making them look even more fascinating.
The sun seems so small
But the colours spread themselves
Lighting the clouds
Telling them morning has arrived.
The sun looks like a fresh orange
Cut in half
Its rays flood the land.
They awake the birds from their sleep
And make the sea sparkle like a thousand diamonds
It slowly gets higher
Dew glistens on the damp grass
Now all of the sun appears
The landscape is exposed
Fresh and ready to start another day
There it stops
Hanging in the middle of the pale blue sky
Just like a lost orange
Beside a puddle of water
The world is awake
So am I?

Charlotte Anderson (11)
St Francis RC School, Maldon

MY MUDSKIPPER

It swims around as happy as can be,
Its legs are strong and body stout,
Its eyes stick out the top of its head,
Looking around for prey to catch.

In the wild in the mangrove swamp,
It will hop and jump for all to see,
With herons watching over,
Hungrily
It's my mudskipper.

Isaac Barry (10)
St Francis RC School, Maldon

SUMMER'S HERE

Summer comes hip hooray!
I've been waiting for it night and day,
A swim here, a sunbathe there,
I've been waiting forever, I've been waiting I swear.

Autumn, winter, spring, here it comes.
Summer's here I put up my thumbs,
I see the sun, no clouds for miles,
The swimming pool starts to pile.

Summer's here, spring's away,
Now I go in my garden to lay,
The birds are singing,
The people are swinging,
Summer is definitely here.

The sun goes down , it's time to go,
I don't want to, no, no!
The birds are gone,
The sun is down,
Tomorrow will be another day
                                    in summer!
Rosalind McKenna (11)
St Francis RC School, Maldon

THE FOREST STORM

The wind roared through the trees
Like a roaring raging fire expanding from tree to tree,
Clapping thunder roars through the sky,
Like an injured beast roaring in pain,
Clouds as black as charcoal floating in the sky.

> I walk under the swaying trees,
> The rain pours down which feels like
> > flint hitting my face,
> I dive to shelter against this bleak weather.

Lightning strikes a tree,
The clouds begin to separate,
The blue sky breaks through,
Then the bright sun appears,
The storm is over, all is quiet.

Marcus Mann (10)
St Francis RC School, Maldon

THE BULLY

Here he comes,
He's just grabbed my bag.
He's thrown it to his so-called friend.
They're playing piggy-in-the middle with me.

I feel horrible, I'm really upset.
Why can't they just leave me alone?
What have I ever done to him?
Why don't they just pick on someone else?

I know what I'll do,
I'll tell my dad.
He'll walk me to school
Then that bully will leave me alone.

My dad did come.
That bully just ran away.
I don't think he'll pick on me again.

Stuart Gear (11)
St Francis RC School, Maldon

THE SCHOOL BULLY

Colin is the school bully,
He picks on this girl called Milly,
Milly is so very smart,
(She is especially good at art),
He waits at the old school gates,
Waiting for poor Milly Bates,
Milly looks scared, she looks unhappy,
He stands there with his dog named Pappy,
Pappy growls, Colin looks mad,
Milly's thinking 'Oh how sad,'
Finally she faces her fears,
Walking past him with her eyes full of tears,
Colin walks in front of her trying to look so cool,
But then he sticks his foot out and makes Milly fall,
Then his mum came round the corner and suddenly said
'Come here Colin you're going home to bed!'

Emily Broadhurst (11)
St Francis RC School, Maldon

FRIENDS

Some friends are good
Some friends are bad
If they are bad
They sometimes make you sad
I hate bullies because they are nasty
Some bullies can make you frightened.

Friends are nice, they're there for you
Sometimes you have a friend to lose.
Friends stick up for you when you are hurt
Some people don't have them when you need them
So you always need a friend, no matter what.

Nikki Everitt (11)
St Francis RC School, Maldon

PUDDING

I sit patiently in the wooden chair,
Smelling the pudding I think nice thoughts,
Then I see my mummy holding a
brown hot cake,
Then I see smoke firing off it.

It moves towards me,
And then *bang!*
It lands right in front of me,
I pick up my silver spoon,
And I dig in,
I bring it towards my mouth and
Boom! It's gone.

Maria Prewer (10)
St Francis RC School, Maldon

THE SMILING PEN

One day I went to the shop,
I had just 20p,
Then a pen appeared from nowhere,
Just the one for me.

It was blue and green and yellow,
The colours to match my file,
But then, I must say, I saw something strange,
I saw, it had a smile.

First the mouth then the eyes,
Then I saw the nose,
I really, really wanted that pen,
No one else had one of those.

I'd show it off to all my friends,
They'd say 'Wow it's cool,'
I would be the talk of the class,
Instead of the class fool.

I checked the price to see that it,
Was only 21p,
I ran back home but the door was locked,
So I couldn't fetch any more money.

I walked down the street very sadly,
When I saw a penny, just one,
I picked it up and ran to the shop,
To find that the pen had gone.

Jackie Stretton (11)
St Francis RC School, Maldon

THE PARK

My friend and I love going to the park
It's good for sunbathing in summer
And good for snowballing in winter
Feeding the ducks after school
We've had lots of fun-times at the park.

Playing hide-and-seek behind the trees
Climbing round the climbing frames
Pretending we're great explorers
We'll have a picnic there and give the
leftovers to the birds
We've had lots of fun times at the park.

Throwing stones into the pond
Picking up leaves and throwing them at each other
Rolling around in the mud
And splashing in puddles with our wellies
We've had lots of fun-times at the park.

Lucy Brown
St Francis RC School, Maldon

TIGER, TIGER

Running through the jungle
with sway and sight, I see a tiger in my sight
feeding her cubs at last.
Then some monkeys swinging from tree to tree,
what a great sight!
Tiger, tiger burning bright in the sunlight,
with your fur coat so orange and bright.

Laura More (11)
St Mary's RC JMI School, Hornchurch

FLOATING IN SPACE

Here I am floating in space,
I need your help,
I've seen an alien,
Without a face.

I'm starving, I'm starving,
I smell something good,
What can it be?
Look I see,
A Milky Way bar,
It doesn't look far.

As I started walking,
It seemed very far,
Maybe I shouldn't
Catch that big Milky Bar.

Ahead in the distance,
I see a twinkling star,
I do hope
It is not far.

Oh look at the time,
I really must go,
I hope to be home,
For dinner you know.

Rebecca Joy O'Leary (10)
St Mary's RC JMI School, Hornchurch

PLANETS

Up in the colossal sky,
Where the stars are so high
And the moon is shining brightly,
Up there somewhere,
Are the planets of my dreams.
Mercury hot like the biggest fire,
Venus brown as if it's burning,
Earth so busy you can't compare it,
Mars is red but getting cooler,
Jupiter big with mighty rings,
Saturn so cold the rings are made of ice,
Uranus green (the sun is so small now)
Neptune the prettiest of them all.
Pluto ice-cold and dark, it's hard to imagine,
Up in the colossal sky,
Where the stars are so high
And the moon is shining brightly.

Ailish Ginty (10)
St Mary's RC JMI School, Hornchurch

BEST FRIENDS

Best friends are what every child needs
They are great fun and really cool
You make them at home
And at school
Best friends are there if you stumble and fall
They're there for help and guidance if you call.

My best friend is Perrie
She's really kind and caring
She is always there for me
She can also be outgoing and daring
Perrie is friendly and sharing
We go around together pairing.

She doesn't like swearing
Not like some
It's cool to hang around with her
Because she's so much fun.

Lara Freeman (11)
St Mary's RC JMI School, Hornchurch

HOW IT SEEMS

In the distant sky
Silvery stars swim across
The Milky Way!
The eerie moon glows and
Lights up the galaxy!
My favourite planet
Has to be delicious
Mars!
All those shimmering
Milky Way stars.
I always see a sparkling star burst
Through the eerie skies.
If only I could
Take flight
And take a huge chunk
From the tantalising
Milky Way.
Thinking about the Galaxy
Always makes me hungry!
All those lovely
Chocolate bars!
I wish I lived in Mars!
Sadly that's all a dream.
I wish space was how it seemed!

Anne Edwards (11)
St Mary's RC JMI School, Hornchurch

TIGER'S LIFE

People say I'm grumpy and I'm always humpy,
They say I have huge big feet with great wide eyes,
And when I walk I take huge strides.
They say I must be baking in my huge furry coat,
With my huge stripy pattern covering my throat.
But you are always shooting at me, trying to get me,
Won't you just let me be,
And try to forget me?
While I'm chasing round trying to get some food,
You're always shooting at me,
That's why I'm in this mood.

Kelly Rudd (11)
St Mary's RC JMI School, Hornchurch

RAINFOREST POEM

If we cut down the rainforest
it will be a big shame
and a pain
because there will be no rain.
We cut down the trees
and disturb the bees
then the cattle come
and there's a battle
against the Indians and the cattle.
When the cattle have gone
the Indians are grumpy
because the ground is lumpy.
The proud and graceful monkeys
will have nowhere to look at the sight
because there will be no height.

Lucy Fleming (11)
St Mary's RC JMI School, Hornchurch

THE RAINFOREST POEM

In the rainforest where it's steamy
monkeys swing from tree to tree
and little lizards crawl up your knee.
Where tigers pounce on their prey
and giant pandas eat all day.
All the fruits you can eat
and little animals you can meet.
Beautiful plants, all shapes and sizes
with little bugs on them.
Frogs, flies all live here too,
but some of these
animals are nearly
extinct because of us.
We cut down trees
and tear up their homes
and all that are left of them are bones.

Stewart Mundy (10)
St Mary's RC JMI School, Hornchurch

THE RAINFOREST AND ITS WILDLIFE

In the rainforest monkeys swing from tree to tree,
but down the on ground bugs live happily.
You may not like them, but they like you,
jumping up your legs and into your shoe.
Wild animals wait for food,
you better watch out because they might get you.
Indian people live here in the rain,
they care about the forest and the animals the same.
The rain comes down every day
but it's still hot here in the rain.

Siobhan Mahoney (10)
St Mary's RC JMI School, Hornchurch

THE ANIMAL KINGDOM

The tiger is so efficient
But the fox is sly,
The lion is the king so proud and elegant,
The elephant is so strong
It can uproot a tree,
The rhino can charge down anything in sight,
The jaguar is spotty so too is the leopard,
But the panther is as black as the night sky.
Some of these are big, while others are titchy and small
Some of these can climb up high
While others just crawl.
The whales swim with fear of the humans up above,
The great white shark is even terrified of us.
All these animals stay in groups or shoals
But when one goes the others are soon to follow.
Some of these animals can be deadly,
Some can be fast,
But all these animals belong to us,
So make their lives last.

Danny McEvoy (11)
St Mary's RC JMI School, Hornchurch

THE WHITE OWL

Very quiet on a branch of a tree,
Look at the white owl
Just staring at me.

Its big yellow eyes
And its lovely white feathers,
Make it glow in that
Beautiful dark sky.

It swoops down to get me
I have no hope,
In a few seconds
Squeak, squeak, it's got me.

Daniel Alexander (10)
St Mary's RC JMI School, Hornchurch

THE TIGER

The tiger creeps slowly
Into the reeds to make the kill
For its supper.
He looks for an easy kill
'Ah ah' thinks the tiger
As he looks at his choice, now
He has chosen his prey
He moves in for the kill.
The tiger's mouth opens and he shows
His horrifying, gigantic, sharp jaws.
Saliva drips out of his mouth,
It's time, time to make the move
As he leaps out from the reeds
He gives a loud roar
Which deafens his prey.
As he lands his
Prey runs for its life.
The gigantic tiger lands on
His prey with
A quick snap of his
Jaws and the animal is
Dead.
All is quiet in the jungle.

Sam Morrison (11)
St Mary's RC JMI School, Hornchurch

THE RAINFOREST POEM

Radical rainforest, big tall trees,
Beautiful flowers, light shaded leaves.
Hidden bugs, as well as animals,
Snakes slither on the ground, in and out of big tall tree roots,
Catching their prey.
In goes the bite,
Look at that sight,
Away it goes for another bite.
Thumping footsteps on the ground,
Pounding paws with sharp claws.
Look at the tiger
And look at those beady red eyes,
And black stripes.

Luke Linehan (11)
St Mary's RC JMI School, Hornchurch

THE RAINFOREST

In the rainforest
there are lots of animals and plants,
but soon they will be all extinct,
and it will not be a pretty rainforest anymore.
Monkeys jumping from tree to tree,
but soon they'll get shot for their meat.
Animals crawling through the grass
catching their prey at last.
Cutting down trees to make a road
chip, chop, all the axes go.
Trees falling to the ground,
what a terrible sound.

Natalie Morrison (10)
St Mary's RC JMI School, Hornchurch

THE SPOILT RAINFOREST

Where has the forest gone?
Machines have come that weigh a ton,
Cutting down trees to make a road,
Chip, chop the axes go.

Down tumble trees that once stood tall,
Creaking and cracking as they fall.
Plunging down, once 30 feet high,
Whilst thousands of others that once touched the sky
Are felled by the trees that are toppling down,
Crashing and crumbling to the ground.

The forest that once stood rich and full,
Is being knocked down for no reason at all.

Animals dart and scamper alone,
Running away from the place that was home.
Hungry and starving and frightened they are,
Trying to dodge new lorries and cars.

Searching around, desperate for food,
Failing to find anything in the dying tree wood,
Whilst men with guns, search and shoot,
Made alert at a single owl's hoot.

Then off they all go without a single care,
Leaving the forest, lifeless and bare.

Gemma Hawkins (11)
St Mary's RC JMI School, Hornchurch

THE TIGER

A tiger's eyes glowing bright, beaming all around him,
Watching out for prey passing by near him,
He's ready to pounce out and eat any kind of meat,
His glowing eyes never stop searching.
His silky soft fur glistening bright,
His giant paws taking giant strides,
Then he hears the noise of the hunters coming,
He runs and hides,
He does not want to be like his friends.
Dead!

Lucy Flynn (11)
St Mary's RC JMI School, Hornchurch

ELEPHANTS

An elephant is big and fat
grey and strong,
a mammoth you see.
Grass for their breakfast, leaves for tea,
don't eat meat, they're herbivores,
with big ivory tusks and long trunks,
with a memory bigger than all of us.
They're big, they're tough,
they could kill us.
With big flappy ears,
great long legs,
big thudding feet.

An elephant never forgets.

Ben Adams (11)
St Mary's RC JMI School, Hornchurch

KITTY CAT

At night you hear a purring, by the fire it may be,
When it has stopped you know she has gone out.
The cat flap you hear
The flap of the door and a miaow and she's gone out.
You hear her soon come in and miaow again
Getting you out of bed.
She has probably come in for some food or cat biscuits,
Well all cats normally come in for that reason
If they are not that well, what a weird cat she is!
A squeak in the hall you know she's got a mouse,
That is why I love cats because they are furry, weird,
I can't leave them alone.

Jane Stonell (10)
St Mary's RC JMI School, Hornchurch

SPARKLING SATURN

Oh what a beautiful planet I am,
I sparkle and twinkle at night-time
When your sleepy heads are dreaming.
The stars think I'm dazzling
The thin layers of ice around me
Look like crystal when the stars twinkle.
The Galaxy is like an atmosphere of diamonds
As I speak,
Jupiter says I'm a show-off!
But I think he's jealous,
I think all the other planets and stars
Want to be just like me.
Before you wake I give off my
Silver beams as I zoom around the sun.

Amy McLeavy (10)
St Mary's RC JMI School, Hornchurch

CRUELTY TO FOXES

The cry of the bugle,
Hounds barking,
The horses' hooves pounding on the ground,
The hunters galloping around on their horses,
The foxes are terrified,
Running around frantically,
Running down their holes.
The hunter sees a fox,
They chase the fox,
Tiring him out,
Chasing him through rivers,
He goes down his hole,
They start digging,
The fox's heart starts beating faster and faster,
They catch him
And feed him to the hounds,
This is so cruel,
I wonder how the hunter would feel
If someone was chasing him?

Joe Wilson (11)
St Mary's RC JMI School, Hornchurch

ALIENS FROM OUTER SPACE

I'm floating in space,
Like I'm in some kind of race.
I'm not going fast,
Then I'm caught in some blast
And catapulted to Mars.

I see a satellite dish,
And hope it's filming me, I wish.
Then some alien from outer space
Comes right down at me with an ugly face.

I blast to the moon with the help of a giant spoon,
Then I see some aliens from the planet Rotten Rocky
What do they carry, ray-guns or zappers,
Their ships look like they're a horde of attackers.

But what we've got to remember is that
Space is the final frontier and wherever we are,
Wherever we go, those aliens will always be near.

Tyrone Patten-Walsh (10)
St Mary's RC JMI School, Hornchurch

THE LIVING RAINFOREST

The trees reach to the sky
And the monkeys are in disguise.
The bees are in the trees
And explorers have grubby knees.
The falling of the leaves
It makes the explorers sneeze.
Insects fly up their knees
They crawl through shrubs
They all start to shudder
They land in a river
With freezing cold quiver.
Then they cut and find a hut
And then they go to sleep.
They wake up in the morning
And they all start yawning
And a leopard jumps in
And starts mauling.
Some people see
A yellow cat
That is very fat.

Damian Jones (10)
St Mary's RC JMI School, Hornchurch

THE ASTEROID BELT

The asteroid belt
Is like a shell
Running helter-skelter
Moving around with no help
If one falls it is likely to melt
You would yelp

Help!
So keep out of the asteroid belt!

Christopher Cable (10)
St Mary's RC JMI School, Hornchurch

SECRET AGENT

Sly, silent,
A secret agent hides in a shadowy corner,
Following a suspect, mysterious as he goes,
With magnifying glass at hand.
Codes and crimes galore,
Using gadgets more and more.

Master of disguise an agent has to be,
On the look-out for secret files
And clues that help him see.
Solving mysteries, he's on the case,
But never too keen to show his face.

Private lairs lay in wait to be explored.
Criminals on the loose,
Dial 999 he's always there to help
You when you call.

Perrie McDowell (10)
St Mary's RC JMI School, Hornchurch

JURASSIC JUNGLE

Somewhere in this awful place,
There must be a sign or a line of pine
To an exit in this awful place.
Deep down in the Jurassic jungle there is a Jurassic mongoose
Which will eat you alive if you are a goose.
So if you're a goose beware, don't move if you hear a snare
Of a Jurassic mongoose beware, beware,
You're in for a scare!

Craig Midson (11)
St Mary's RC JMI School, Hornchurch

LIONS, THE KING OF THE BEASTS

Africa the place where cheetahs, leopards and lions live.
This is one place you don't want to live.
The lion is known as king of the beasts,
All the animals fear this great beast.
The lions' roar can be heard from six miles away.
Most of the lionesses do the hunting,
While lions guard against enemies.
Lionesses pounce at their prey
To surprise human beings and antelope,
That will be their tea.
Lions have elegant fur,
And they are camouflaged in the background.
It would be a disaster if lions were extinct.
There would be no king of the beasts.

Daniel Needham (10)
St Mary's RC JMI School, Hornchurch

ME

I have blue eyes just like the sky,
I have brown hair just like the wood,
I am of medium height just like a big adult mountain bike,
I have a good sense of humour just like a happy schoolteacher,
I am funny just like a clown with a red nose,
I like sweets just like a lollipop lady,
I like swimming just like a fish,
I like music just like a pop star,
I like acting just like an actress,
I like going to the cinema just like a film star,
I am as brave as a lion.

Sharlene Power (11)
St Mary's RC JMI School, Hornchurch

TIGERS

Tigers are fierce
Tigers are big
They have big fangs like teeth
They have big claws
Tigers stay low
Tigers stay still
Their eyes glow in the dark, like a shining light
Tigers are strong
Tigers are tough
They are always listening
And always alert.
They stay still and low for their prey
Tigers have razor-sharp black stripes and gingery fur.
Tigers may look cute but trust me they're not.
Their stripes are camouflaged in with the grass.

Simon Smith (11)
St Mary's RC JMI School, Hornchurch

THE LONGEST STREAM

Long, long stream,
Where are you found?
Over hills or in a mountain,
Or deep underground.
I see you sparkle, flowing down
In a place where you are found.
I've travelled high
And I've travelled low
Just to see your glittery glow.
I stop and stare and watch you flow
Where you go nobody knows,
I'll keep searching no matter what
Because your glow means a lot.

Christine Scott (10)
St Mary's RC JMI School, Hornchurch

THE RAINFOREST RIVER

If I was a river, look how terrified I would be.
I'd be flowing high feeling like I'd touch the sky.
I'd be on a mountain top one day seeing birds catch their prey.
Tall trees I see, such a beautiful view.
Animals running wild, some camouflaged, some not.
Down below snails and snakes would slither slow.
That's the noise they make.
Trickle, trickle, the sound I'd make seizing my chance day by day.
I'd pounce and bounce, splash and bash, trying to get into the sea.
When I'd seen the sea a terrible look would run over me.
The smell was disgusting, it smelt like fish
And then I'd see it, crisp packets, bottles, litter everywhere
And suddenly crash! I was in the sea.

Kelly Gerbaldi (10)
St Mary's RC JMI School, Hornchurch

INTO SPACE

Three, two, one blast-off!
We are going into space
To land on the moon's face
Passing the stars, the Milky Way Restaurant
Where we are sure to meet some aliens
We see shooting stars on our way
Which makes it look like a bright day
Clouds like cotton wool pass us by
See us as we shoot by
Far below the Earth looks like a carpet of brown and green
With miniature houses that look neat and tiny
The sun glows brightly as we circle by
We do see wonderful things as we shoot by in the sky
Before we know it our trip is over
And we land in the sea at Dover.

Claudio Zeolla (10)
St Mary's RC JMI School, Hornchurch

ALIENS AGAIN

Here they come,
Those wretched men
With five fingers and toes.
With sprouty shoots out of their heads.
With two eyes and only one nose.

With their noisy blasters,
And things that go whoosh,
Like our *swongy* casters
They go up with a push.

I think they're called human beings
They have weird names like Pat and Dean
They speak very funny
And have paper called money
I think they live on Earth!

Nicola Hawkins (10)
St Mary's RC JMI School, Hornchurch

SATURN

Space has many planets all beautiful, I'm sure,
The most enchanting is Saturn,
Rings of ice so delicate and thin,
A ball of gas, stunning to look at,
Saturn has eleven moons, the second largest planet,
Stars shine around bright and bold,
But Saturn beats them all.
She glides around the sun like a ballroom dancer round the hall
Stars agree with me,
She's a delightful sight to see
Uranus (the next planet in line)
Says she's very fine.
Neptune never has much to say,
But he thinks she's as beautiful as a summer's day.
Pluto isn't often heard but he says she flies like a bird.
Jupiter the largest planet in the solar system.
He thinks she's a fantasy,
Mars doesn't have a good view,
But has been told she's spectacular by a few.
Venus and Mercury love her so.
Well that concludes it, Saturn's the best!
So I suppose she beats the rest.

Laura Wood (11)
St Mary's RC JMI School, Hornchurch

PEACOCK

A peacock is a proud bird
His body is the darkest shade of blue,
His face is the colour of the sea with white and black stripes upon
his eye.
The blackest feathers crown his head.
Upon his back is the most fantastic display of colours, purples, violets,
blues, green and orange.
A peacock is the most beautiful, elegant, graceful bird,
His feathers are the symbol of Hera, the Greek goddess,
They are proud and majestic when spread like a fan.
These feathers that entice man to steal nature's gift
And leave the proud peacock sad
No more to spread his fantastic fan of majestic feathers
No more to entice his hen.

Charlotte Carver (10)
St Mary's RC JMI School, Hornchurch

THOR, GOD OF THUNDER

It is night, a black curtain sweeps across the sky,
It moves so slowly and quietly no one sees,
Thor God of Thunder bangs his hammer hard,
He wakes small children and they cry tears of fear and terror,
The wind howls
A storm begins
Thor is working hard with anger
He becomes sleepy
As the sun spreads across the sky
Thor lays down to rest
And all is well in the skies.

Claire Chisholm (10)
St Mary's RC JMI School, Hornchurch

OUTER SPACE

Five, four, three, two, one. Blast-off!
A magical rocket
Zooming and whooshing in the air,
Up above the twinkly stars.
Up, up, up it goes.
It landed on a gloomy moon.
Its fiery vicious engine stopped
Then the astronauts' ears popped.
Out they come!
Floating and bouncing all about
Up and down up and down they go.
The moon was like a silhouette
Dusty, dirty and don't forget
A speaking moon, so gloomy.
'How are you?' said a gloomy speaking voice.
'You are stepping on my nose,' said the moon.

Ainhoa Keskin (10)
St Mary's RC JMI School, Hornchurch

COSMIC

Oh cosmic, oh cosmic
What are you?
The stars or are you the flowers?
No
I am the stars and the flowers
I can be anything I want to be
Because that's what cosmic means
I can be anything in the universe
Because I am cosmic.

Gareth Lowe (10)
St Mary's RC JMI School, Hornchurch

PLACES AN ALIEN GOES ON HOLIDAY

I am an alien, I like to go away
I like to visit other planets
Like Pluto, Saturn, Venus and Mars
I'm a ginger-haired alien
I'm skinny and bright-faced.
I have one eye and three legs
Seven toes, two fingers
I wear one shoe and my eye is blue
Tomorrow I'm going to Jupiter,
I hope the weather's nice!
My friend Fred said it was really nice there
There's one place I'm not going to
And that's the sun!
For I would get too space-burned
And I would be the only one there.
I've always wanted to go to Uranus
But I've never had the chance.
Maybe I'll go in two light years
I just can't wait!
Now I have to go to Jupiter
I've really enjoyed your stay
And I hope I see you again some day.

Keighley Harding (10)
St Mary's RC JMI School, Hornchurch

COSMIC

It was eerie, dark and misty,
Everything was quietly resting.
It was all very interesting
On a planet unknown.
It looked like nothing was here
Until we came near, to the alien!
He had three eyes, one mouth, one nose,
An ear on one head
Just looking at the sight
Made us almost drop dead.
He was ugly and small
But he was friendly and started to run and call.
We followed him over a mountain and into a fountain
Of stars, lasers, houses, supermarkets and aliens.
More aliens.
They came up to us and said 'Zomoday! Zomoday!'
We went to explore the town
And were amazed at what we found.
They ate like us, drank like us and lived like us.
Then we remembered the rocket!
Had we turned it off?
We heard the engine roar and take off
The aliens just laughed and pointed up.
While we got angry and fed-up.
Now we are *prisoners* up, up, up, in space!

Adam Locke (10)
St Mary's RC JMI School, Hornchurch

MY FRIEND THE ALIEN

My friend the alien is very refined,
He's always there when you need him
But he sometimes trails behind.
You may think he is slimy
You may think he is cantankerous
But he's also very kind
One day he came to see me
In his usual friendly way
And I was on my way to school
In my usual way of wanting to be good and clever
And out he popped
From behind a wall
And I jumped and fell!
Suddenly my friend vanished into thin air
I called him but he did not answer
And sadly I never heard from him
Then later that week
I wrote a missing poster
And it said
'Missing Alien
4 eyes, 3 ears,
2 mouths, and 2 horns.
If found please return'.

Racheal Miranda (10)
St Mary's RC JMI School, Hornchurch

AN ALIEN MEETS AN ASTRONAUT

One cold night an astronaut met an alien.
The alien had eight eyes, four noses, two mouths, sixteen legs
Seven hands, fifteen heads and a
Multicoloured tongue!
He looked hideous
With red and black spots,
The astronaut ran to his moon buggy,
Then the alien started to cry
'Boo-hoo, hoo,
I only want a friend, I am friendly really!'
The astronaut started to bounce,
He wasn't on Earth he was on the moon!
His name was Googie Zooga!
The astronaut made friends with the alien
At tea, at the alien's house.
Everyone was happy
When the astronaut had to go back to Earth
The Alien came too!
Googie Zooga,
Was yellow, green
And purple and a nice colour
Gold.

Emily Rodgers (10)
St Mary's RC JMI School, Hornchurch

MY FRIEND THE ALIEN

My friend's a weird friend,
A wacky friend but a wise friend.
He has seven eyes, six arms and six legs
He is slimy, hairy, bog-eyed
And he came from above,
Not heaven but from
Madness Monster Land
Mars!
I went to Alien school
With him one winter's day
But then they said,
'Excuse me, you have to pay!'
Me and my friend have been to the moon,
To Mars, Saturn, and Jupiter.
But yesterday he said,
'Sorry, I have to go.'
And flew off to where,
No one knows.

Rachael Grainger (10)
St Mary's RC JMI School, Hornchurch

SPACE

Beyond Earth's atmosphere,
So deep in the sky,
So much space to fill your eyes,
So much to explore.

Rockets to get there,
Spacesuits to wear
A lot of adjustments
When you get there.

So many planets
Still to explore
So many people still
Volunteer to go.

Damian Riordan (10)
St Mary's RC JMI School, Hornchurch

A BABY ALIEN GETS LOST

I am very round, small and stout,
I'm only a baby, so I can't shout,
I looked around but this place was very strange,
The aliens were from a different range.
I started to cry and I felt very sad,
If I saw my mum and dad I'd feel very glad,
This place was shining, shimmering, dazzling,
And it was silver like me,
But it had a face,
And was as happy as could be.
This place had craters and was as hard as rock,
It was crystallised, foggy and smelt like a sock.
It was also round, small, and stout,
And it couldn't shout.
I also knew it was moving about,
Then I saw my mum and dad,
I felt now, very glad.
They explained to me it was the moon,
This silvery place, with a big face,
That was my first word,
'The Moon.'

Siân Nash (10)
St Mary's RC JMI School, Hornchurch

AN ASTRONAUT AND AN ALIEN IN SPACE

There once was an astronaut
That flew up to space,
He had a silvery spacesuit on
He also had big boots.
Space was empty, gloomy and dark,
Apart from the planets that glowed in the dark.
He could see Saturn
With its big ring around it,
He could also see Venus and Mars.
But he landed on Neptune
And decided to set out.
He saw something glowing,
But couldn't make out what it was.
He went a bit closer
And the thing turned around,
He realised what it was,
He had found an alien!
The alien was strange,
With three fingers on each hand.
He was green and short
And had yellow spots all over him,
But he was sad.
He said he was lost and needed to be on Mars,
So the astronaut took the alien back to Mars
And the alien said 'Thank you very much.'
Then the astronaut went home to Earth.

Katie McGuire (10)
St Mary's RC JMI School, Hornchurch

ASTRONAUT MEETS AN ALIEN

There was an astronaut
Who flew into space.
He went by Venus
And fiery Mars.
He saw a gigantic blob of green
He flew down
And had a peep
What he saw was an alien
With six gigantic eyes
Four fat, shaky legs
With two mouths.
The astronaut laughed
And so did the alien.

Daniel Ruocco (10)
St Mary's RC JMI School, Hornchurch

THE SUNDAY STAR

On a Sunday night
I saw a star
And what a bright star it was
With a shining brightness
Like a booming light
From the powerful sun
Or the sparkle of the ice
Which surrounds the glow of Saturn.
It seemed to look at me as I lay
And gave a shine to my eye
It will be waiting
For me
The Sunday night star.

Davinia R D Vincent (10)
St Mary's RC JMI School, Hornchurch

SPACE

Space is high up in the sky
Can we see it, no, not I.
Spaceships we've heard
Of whizzing around.
All shapes and sizes
Is what we have found.
Are there aliens high
Above us running around
All green and scary?
I do not know.
They could be ordinary
Just like us, but until
I have been there
We will just have to guess.

Marc O'Sullivan (10)
St Mary's RC JMI School, Hornchurch

MY FUNKY FURRY FRIENDS

They're funky,
They're furry,
They're really, really cuddly,
They live on the planet Hug-Cug
They look like teddy bears,
They feel like teddy bears,
In fact I think I'm in love.

They're fat,
They're round,
They're my little friends.

Their planet is clean and tidy,
Not at all like ours,
They're friendly,
They're kind
They're very polite
It's a shame I can't stay all night.

Natasha Doughty (10)
St Mary's RC JMI School, Hornchurch

JUPITER'S ALIENS

'Help me! Help me!' says Bobby
From the gross, half-sphere shape-nosed alien
Who is coming to eat me?
The blue and black Alien.
With sharp claws
Is coming to whip me
Into his pie
But I who needed to get away from him,
Ran as fast as my legs could take me.
He has a pointy chin.
There was sweat coming out of him.
Deadly teeth came out to greet me.
A bony mouth as he came.
His diagonal hair
Which gave me a scare chased me
And I zoomed out of sight
As his powers zoomed round him
Help me! Help me!
He gives me a scare!

Jason Richard Summers (10)
St Mary's RC JMI School, Hornchurch

UGLY ALIENS

I saw this thing
Come out of the mists.
What on earth was this?
Disgusting, revolting
What else can I say.
It was green with red spots.
He was quite hairy
And very, very scary
But before I said anything,
He invited me over for tea
But the cup started floating
Up and down and all around!
I couldn't keep it on the ground
So I ate my curry.
Ooh! That does taste nice.
'Filolo,' it said
Whatever it meant.
I don't know but I'm sure it meant
I'm your friend.

Hazel Evens (10)
St Mary's RC JMI School, Hornchurch

SPACE HOLIDAY

Hello my name is Natalie
Let me talk about my holiday in space
It's a magnificent place
With a cheesy Moon.
Me and my mum tried some
Oh it's lovely in a bun.

I think I saw an alien
With big watery eyes
Which glowed in the dark
I ran and told my mum
But she didn't believe me
Oh well I would love to
Go back to space
That weird and wonderful place.

Natalie Dellamura (10)
St Mary's RC JMI School, Hornchurch

ASTRONAUT

I love to fly in space,
I explore the milk-white moon,
I ride the pinball comets,
I'm visiting Mercury soon,
I sit on Mars when the Sun beckons,
A tan in two seconds.
I'm visiting a Mars dweller
With a waddle, named Stella,
He will have boxes of wheat,
A heart that doesn't beat,
With a push of my feet,
I'd yell, 'When again should we meet.'
Then advance to the Earth quite primly
The Universe is great.
And to think of its fate,
But I really have to admit,
That I'd rather sit
At home where I have normal weight.

Simon Gotman
St Mary's RC JMI School, Hornchurch

MOON AND SUN

I am the sun scorching and bright
I shine by day but not by night,
I shine on the Earth making it light.
If it weren't for me it would always be night.
I'm like a giant fireball made of burning gasses.
Don't come too close to me
Or you'll burn to ashes.

I've done my job
I need some rest
Now it's the moon's turn to do her best.
I am the moon, silvery and white
I don't shine by day but shine by night
Casting my eerie shadows when it's not light
And they give people a horrible fright.
There's one big job that's up to me
I am in control of the tides of the sea.

Night-time's over,
My work is done
So I hand you over
To my friend the Sun.

Matthew Dwyer (11)
St Mary's RC JMI School, Hornchurch

THE FLOATING MAN

There was once a man called Laced,
Who liked to walk through space.
He thought it fascinating to sit on the moon
And eat yoghurt with a spoon.
Then all of a sudden to his great surprise
The yoghurt floated and changed its size.

He went to see planet Mars,
Instead he bumped into lots of stars
On the planet Mars, people were eating chocolate bars
Maybe I should go home after all,
It's been a bad day for us all.

Emma Crafer (10)
St Mary's RC JMI School, Hornchurch

CANDY HEAVEN

I think that I'm in heaven,
All my dreams are coming true,
Skittles and Double Deckers,
Pear drops and chocolate chews,
A mountain the size of Everest,
All stacked with crisps and sweets,
This is really unbelievable,
Talk about treats!
The shelves are stacked with Crunchies,
Milky Ways and Opal Fruits,
Fruit Pastilles full of juice,
Soleros and chocolatey Magnums,
They really are my favourite,
Unfortunately though,
I cannot stay long,
Homework beckons,
Back to reality
I suppose I'll just have to settle for sweet dreams!

Nicole Shanley (11)
St Mary's RC JMI School, Hornchurch

SILVERY STARS

Shimmery, shining stars
Stretched across the sky
You can't count them with your eyes
The beautiful bright stars
Shine in the night
To beam out with all their might.
Their silvery beams
Like little light bulbs
Lighting up the sky
Tormenting little stars they're everywhere
You can go from
Pluto to Mercury and back
But you'll never count those little diamond lights.

Sarah Forbes (11)
St Mary's RC JMI School, Hornchurch

FLYING IN MY ROCKET

I was flying in my rocket
Spinning in space
When I saw a big comet
Heading across space
It was large and bright
With a ghostly sight
And disappeared into the night.

Kirstie Smith (10)
St Mary's RC JMI School, Hornchurch

FLYING IN SPACE

I went up into space one day,
To meet the stars and moon
But on the way I had to stop because I saw Kracoon.

He was a rather nasty planet
He was made of marble and of granite
He was very big
He wore a green wig
And he never did manage
To put on a smile.

So I moved on from him
And found a planet with a big grin
I asked his name
And he said it was Cane
'That sounds cool,' I said to him
He didn't do anything, just grin and grin!

So I then moved on and came across something weird
He said people called him Fliba Jaba
He didn't have a circle or a ring around him
And unlike Jupiter he had no spot.

I decided to explore
But then I changed my mind
I went back to Earth just to find
That there's really nothing quite like home.

Laura Carter (10)
St Mary's RC JMI School, Hornchurch

LOST IN SPACE

Here I am,
Lost in space
I need your help
Because I haven't got a face.
I smell something nasty
What can it be?
I don't know what it is
Because I can't see.
I'm coming closer to the nasty smell,
It's an alien
He says his name is Grell.
So Grell and I go off to eat
And then we bump into someone's feet.
It's huge, furry, slimy, PH smelly says Grell
Hello my name is Zell
Do you need any help?
Well we wouldn't want a ten ton, smelly,
          slimy, furry animal asking for help
Now would we!
Ah! Oh!
Doug!

Anthony Church
St Mary's RC JMI School, Hornchurch

THE MOON

When I look upon the Moon,
I see a great big white balloon
It turns all different shapes and sizes
And sometimes it gives me great surprises.
Sometimes it's round,
Sometimes it's not,
Sometimes it's cold,
And sometimes it's hot.
It's 1998
The moon is big and great
But one day it might fall apart,
Then it won't be so tough and smart,
I love the moon when it glows at night,
It fills the sky so wonderfully bright.
I'd hate it if the moon did fall,
Because there wouldn't be a moon at all.

Beth Forsey (10)
St Mary's RC JMI School, Hornchurch

MOON

In the blackness of the sky
Zooming to stars and through the sky,
In the distance there it is
A white blob floating in front of my face.
Soon it will go up and up
Into the blackness of space.

Lauren Woolf (10)
St Mary's RC JMI School, Hornchurch

PLANETS

All planets are big and small,
But I think Earth has got it all.
It may be small on the outside
But on the inside it has a wondrous atmosphere.
Mercury is the closest planet to the sun,
I think anyone who lives on there can't be having much fun.
Venus is second closest to the sun,
It must be very hot, I wouldn't like to live there.
Mars that's where I'd like to stay,
Humans may be living there one day.
Jupiter, the big man of the sky, well that's what he says
But of course it isn't a lie.
Saturn, such a beautiful thing,
How does it cope with all those rings?
Uranus a big green planet
The stars that go around it are rapid.
Neptune a wonderful planet big and blue
It's nice for me and you.
Pluto the coldest planet in the line
But you must say it's quite fine.

Grace-Marie Bonnici (11)
St Mary's RC JMI School, Hornchurch

EASTERTIME

Eastertime is fun.
Easter eggs and little chicks that look so sweet.
Eastertime is fun,
Because the night before the Easter Bunny comes.
Eastertime is fun,
Because you have a nice meal.
And maybe a hot-cross bun.

John Jakobsson (10)
Springfield PNEU School

THE HOT SUN

As I saw the sun glitter in the sky
Wishing I was there,
The blazing hot sun
Just sitting in the air.

I sat down with nothing to do,
Children were having fun
I was so bored
Sitting in the sun.

Then a child shouted to me
'Please come and play.'
Then I started to hope
It could always be this way.

In the hot sun.

Charlotte Bilton (10)
Springfield PNEU School

WEATHER

January cold and bitter,
Snowmen we build.
February the same but dark a lot of the time.
March gets brighter, but rain,
The clocks go forward
April some birthdays appear,
The sun is coming near.
Then comes Easter for Christ has risen.
May, the sun is shining bright.
I sunbathe and
I might go swimming.
June the sun is just doing its job
Shining bright.
We could get rain.
July and August are sunny days and
We thank the Lord with praise.
Soon autumn will begin.
October is autumn as well
But some children are not well.
November and December are happy days,
And do we thank the Lord with praise?
Yes we do because Christ,
It's Christ that's born and
I was born close to that
They are both in December,
For mine the 5th and
For Christ the 25th and what a little difference,
And a new season begins
It is cold and bitter once again.

Marie Berry (10)
Springfield PNEU School

THE DARK NIGHT

It's dark at night and the sky comes alight,
The stars are gold in the dark, dark night,
But I still see their peep of a clear gold light.
All on my own in the dark, dark night.

I'm all on my own just me and myself,
In the garden of Nanny Oakshelfs
Nobody's running, playing or singing,
Dancing, jumping or hanging out linen.

It seems forever all by myself,
In the garden of Nanny Oakshelfs
And still those stars are in the sky . . .
But now it's time to say goodbye!

Victoria Louise Currey (10)
Springfield PNEU School

TENT POLES

When we go on holiday
we are always organised
but this time
no way, we were half-way to Devon.
At this point I was really looking forward
to a week's holiday in a tent.
But my dad's thinking, *did we pack the tent poles?*
Then we hear 'Oh no, sorry kids but I forgot the tent poles.'
So at that time it was 7pm,
my Dad said we will have to find
a bed and breakfast
we found one in the end.

Sam Gage (10)
The Priory CP School

THE SPLASH

We went on holiday,
And we went to Palton's Park
We had to wait ages to get on one of the best rides.
This particular ride was called water bump.
About three hours later we got in,
But when we did get in,
It was an absolute catastrophe
I couldn't get the thing to move,
The instructor didn't tell me how to work it
So there I was,
Spinning round and round,
Then it dawned on me!
You had to turn the wheel the opposite way you were spinning,
I zoomed over to where Sara (my sister) was
And bumped her.
The good thing about it was,
All the water was splashed onto her,
Then I went back to spinning
And no matter how hard I tried
I couldn't go straight.
Then my time was up.
But I couldn't get back to where I started.

Elisa Buttle (11)
The Priory CP School

BUYING NEW SHOES

When I was younger,
every time I needed
a new pair of shoes
my mum, sister and my dad
they would take me down
to Chelmsford.
We would go in every
shop looking for shoes.
I would say,
'Can I have this pair?'
My mum would say
'No Hollie, you don't
want blue shoes!'
So I said,
'Can I have this pair?'
Mum would say,
'No, you are certainly not having them,
they are far too expensive.'
'They are only £35.00,'
I would say.
At last we have found
a pair of shoes.
I won't want to go through that
again in a hurry.

Hollie Coppen (11)
The Priory CP School

ME AND MY BIG BROTHER

When I get home
I usually watch TV,
And when my big brother comes home
The trouble starts.
'Give me that last apple'
'No' I said
'Give me that last apple'
'No' I said
'Mum, Andrew hit me on the arm'
'No I didn't'
'Yes you did'
'Stop it you boys'
'Andrew you stay down here,
Jonathan you go upstairs'
Andrew always get away from it
Oh well that's just me and
My big brother.

Jonathan Woollard (10)
The Priory CP School

ME AND THE MOTOR BIKE JUMP

One Saturday afternoon when I was bored
I decided to make a *motor bike jump,*
I thought it was an *excellent* idea,
I began making it
by Saturday night, it was finished for Sunday.
I woke up really early to try the new jump,
I put on my helmet, ran outside,
started up my motor bike, went over the jump
and . . .

Crash, straight in the hedge!
I pulled me and my motor bike out of the hedge
and tried again, this time I went straight over it,
this time I did not go in the hedge,
I went in the cornfield,
my dad wasn't best pleased,
but I didn't blame him because I had churned up the field.
After that I never did have another go on the jump,
I just stuck to the small humps and bumps.

Matthew Smith (11)
The Priory CP School

TOM AND THE HOCKEY STICK

Some Saturdays Sam comes and knocks
for Tom and he gets his skates and says
'Are you coming out' and Tom says 'Yes.'
So we go and knock for Matt,
And his mum says,
'He is playing down Westerings.'
So we were playing at the Grove and Sam said,
'Let's go around the school and skate in the car park.'
As we went there we saw Matt with his friend
in the car park playing hockey and we said,
'Can we play?'
and they said, 'Yes.'
So we played hockey.
Then Tom got hit
he said 'Ow.'

Tom Woodley (11)
The Priory CP School

CORNFLAKES AND PINS

One day I was at school
it was home time.
I was going round my friend's house.
When we got there
we had a bowl of cornflakes.
we were putting the cornflakes in the bowl,
then I put the milk in,
and then waited for Catherine to finish.
We then walked into the lounge
and sat down, in front of us was a sewing machine
and some pins that were Catherine's mum's,
she was sewing a tablecloth.
We started eating,
Catherine was holding the box of pins
to get the piece of cotton out of the box.
She did it and something else,
she dropped all the pins in the bowl of cornflakes.
So I laughed and then I got a spoon and I helped her,
at last we got them out.
So then we carried on eating
and Catherine was just about to take a mouthful
and there was a pin on the spoon.
I said, 'Watch out, a pin!'

Zoë Higgins (11)
The Priory CP School

NEVER THROW ROCKS AT A TREE

One Wednesday my friend was so gutted.
Me, Ali, Tom and Adam went to the park
and you would not believe it if I told you but
here it goes.
Like I said, me, Ali, Tom and Adam were over
the park trying to get acorns out of a tree,
to get them and throw them at each other.
Then I heard, *aahhh*, and it was
Adam shouting as loud as he could.
I said, 'What's wrong?'
Ali said, 'I threw a rock up a tree
and it fell on Adam's head
and split it open.'

Luke Inwood (10)
The Priory CP School

I AM THE DYNAMITE GOALIE

I am the *dynamite* goalie,
here comes a penalty.
Shall I go left?
Shall I go right?
Either way I am the dynamite goalie.
Well, here it comes,
now which way shall I go?
Here I go
to the left
but the ball
goes off to the right.
Into the goal
the ball goes,
perhaps I am not the dynamite goalie.

Sam Bridge (11)
The Priory CP School

DON'T

All parents ever go on about is:
'Don't do this.'
'Don't do that.'
They always say things like
Don't put the television on,
it's a lovely day outside.
But why don't they understand
there's a good film on the TV?
Then they would say something like
'In our day we didn't have television.'
But that was something like
2000 years ago!
All parents ever go on about is:
'Don't do this.'
'Don't do that.'

Adam Foster (10)
The Priory CP School

THE ICE CUBE

About one year ago
I was in the kitchen
When my brother said to me,
'I dare you to eat an ice cube.'
I said, 'OK, watch me!'
So I did, it was so cold
That it stuck to my tongue.
I called Mum, 'Mum, Mum.'
I stuck my tongue out,
Then I had to wait for it to melt
It took ages.

I guess I should have drunk a hot drink really.
But I didn't think of that.
My mum and brother just sat there with a grin and laughed.
My mum and dad said,
'Don't do silly things like that again.'
I said, 'But Mum, Jack told me to.'
'If he told you to jump under a ...'
'Ya, ya.'
I looked down on the couch thinking how I will get him back.

Amy Littmoden (10)
The Priory CP School

THE FIGHT

Zzzzzzzzzzzzzzz
hiss, miaow, hissssss ...
silence.
Miaowwwwww, roawww, roawww!
Bang, bang, bang, miaow
'Aahh someone's coming to get me, ahhhh!'
Thud, thud, thud, thud,
what's happening then and what on earth
could that noise be?
It sounds like the entire police force have come!
Miaowww, oww, oww, oww, roawww.
For goodness sake Mum!
It's only the stupid cat!
All you had to do Shiana was pick her up
and give her to Mum.
Can't I have any peace around here.

Aisling Jarvis (10)
The Priory CP School

THE GREENHOUSE

It was all going fine,
A sunny day,
I was playing football in the garden
With my friend Ben.
He was in goal,
I charged at him,
He brought me down
'Penalty' I cried.
Placing the ball on the spot,
The crowd are going wild.
Running up,
Reach the ball,
Smack.
It shoots past Ben,
Over the fence,
And,
Crash!
Straight through my next door
neighbour's greenhouse window.
I heard a slight muffled cry
from behind me.
'Alastair!'

Alastair Cox (11)
The Priory CP School

SWEET SHOP

I went in the sweet shop
and I bought some sweets
I saw some
bright silver paper.
Dark chocolate.
Hard toffees.
Crunchy crisps.
Fizzy drinks.
Pictures in newspapers.
Smooth magazines.
Funny comics.
Fantastic games.
Colourful gobstoppers.
Nice chewing gum.

Dean Lawday (10)
Theydon Bois CP School

DOWN ON THE FARM

Down on the farm a pig bit my arm
a horse did a wee-wee on my favourite barn
the pig swelled up
and ate my cup.
Clap, clap, clap, clap,
a colour-blind ball made me fall
and I hit a very, very hard wall.
My fruit ball fell into a tank of piranhas
and they ate up all my prize bananas,
then I realised I was on the wrong farm.

Terry Thornhill (10)
Theydon Bois CP School

MY PLANETARIUM

Shining Sun
heat is intense
fire and gas
ever so dense

Mellow Mercury
not atmosphere
little craters
shaped in a sphere

Venomous Venus
goddess of love
heat and fire
burns men from above

Marvellous Mars
craters and bumps
imagined Martians
rock in huge lumps

Gigantic Jupiter
gassy and red
three Earths in red spot
won't fit in *my* bed!

Silky Saturn
many kings
Titan moon
swirls and things

Unbelievable Uranus
gassy and green
dark and cold
ice rings can be seen

Neuter Neptune
blue ball of gas
orbits cross
furthest out comes to pass

Pleasant Pluto
smaller than moon
outermost known
smiley soon

Superb Smiley
unexplored
distantly sighted
curiosity implored

Haley's Comet
tail from the sun
unseen from Saturn
there's only one

Massive Meteorites
metal or rock
craters are formed
plenty in stock!

My planetarium
no one to share
plenty of wonder
please treat with care!

Joane M Cox (11)
Theydon Bois CP School

THE FANTASTIC NUMBER 37

The fantastic number 37
The number 37 is a very magic number. If you multiply
$$37 \times 3 = 111$$
$$37 \times 6 = 222$$
$$37 \times 9 = 333$$
$$37 \times 12 = 444$$
$$37 \times 15 = 555$$
$$37 \times 18 = 666$$
$$37 \times 21 = 777$$
$$37 \times 23 = 888$$
$$37 \times 27 = 999$$
and that's how the number 37 is magic.

Stephen Freestone (10)
Theydon Bois CP School

SPICE GIRLS

Spice Girls are the best
Vicky's the one with the Gucci dress
Emma is so really cool
Mel C needs to go back to school
Geri's the one with the ginger hair
Scary looks like she had a scare.
Spice Girls!

Jamie Tomlin (10)
Theydon Bois CP School

I WOULD LIKE TO LIVE IN THE COUNTRY

I would like to live in the country,
So I could live in a beautiful house.
I would like to explore the cornfield,
So I could find a cute little mouse.
I would like to live in the country,
No noise, no traffic at all,
No busy cars, no traffic lights,
Just silence, that's all!

Amanda Scantlebury (10)
Theydon Bois CP School

THE ANIMALS OF THE WOODS

Into the scented woods we'll go,
See the owls swooping down,
For years there's been no fish in the lake,
Look, a badger, see it's great,
See the woodpecker peck on its tree,
A mole digging for worms,
Can you hear the rabbit stamp in its hole?
What more can you see?
Can you see that the owl has wise eyes?
The squirrel is rushing through the trees,
Now say goodbye to the animals please.

Holly Wells (11)
Westerings Primary School

THE VOLCANO

The lava crackles, pops and
starts to flow,
it is red-hot as it spits and bubbles,
the ground shakes as the
lava pours over the edge,
it gets faster and faster,
rocks crashing down,
the volcano has erupted!

Sarah Culwick (10)
Westerings Primary School

STORM

I hate storms,
They're horrible things,
We know they're not, but
They think they're kings.

Lightning flashes,
Thunder booms,
The lights go out,
In all of the homes.

There are lots of power cuts,
As the rain pours down.
Reservoirs overflow,
Some people drown.

Then it all quietens down,
There's not a soul in sight.
An eerie silence
Has ended the night.

Amy White (11)
Westerings Primary School

STORM

When there is a fierce storm above Saturday Island,
It really is like hell let loose,
The wind whips up the waves on the beach,
Lightning splits the sky in two,
Rain pounds on thatched roofs,
Window-panes shiver and shake.
When morning comes,
There is destruction everywhere . . .

Mark Allen (11)
Westerings Primary School

SPAIN

Spain is a country full of fun,
Plenty of sand and plenty of sun,
Flamenco dancers all around,
Tap, tap, tap a rhythmic sound,
Citrus fruits grow on the land,
At picking time you'll need a hand,
A glass of Spanish wine is nice,
Served with paella, a dish of rice,
In Spain there's always a lot to do,
See for yourself, try something new.

Zoë Walkling (10)
Westerings Primary School

A THEME PARK

Children on rides
Scream and shout,
People running,
All about.
A whiff of doughnuts
Drifts through the air,
A sign for Nemesis,
'Ride if you dare'.
Katie and I
Are finally here,
Though scary rides
Are our biggest fear.
We nervously move into the abyss,
Of the everlasting queue
And rode the terrifying Nemesis,
My mummy was scared too.
Roller-coasters, flying swings,
Roundabouts and all those things,
Teacups, logflume, rapids too,
Haunted house and then the zoo.
On the way to our next ride,
Passed a restaurant and had to decide,
We chose to eat,
And rest our feet.
The pirate ship swings
From side to side.
It makes me nauseous
Just watching the ride.
We finished the day,
With the runaway train,
We've had a fun time,
So we'd like to come again.

Katheryn Seddon (11)
Westerings Primary School